ABC

Colouring and Activity

a

All these things begin with the letter a.
Colour them in.

arrow

ant

apple

astronaut

acorn

alligator

b

All these things begin with the letter b; ball, boat, bag, boy, balloon. Draw lines to match them into pairs.

Who lives here?
Lift the flap to find out.

___ ___ ___ ___

Write the word.

Draw a line between the things that begin with c.
Draw a circle around the things that begin with d.
Colour in the picture.

Colour the things that begin with the letter e.
Draw a circle around the odd one out.

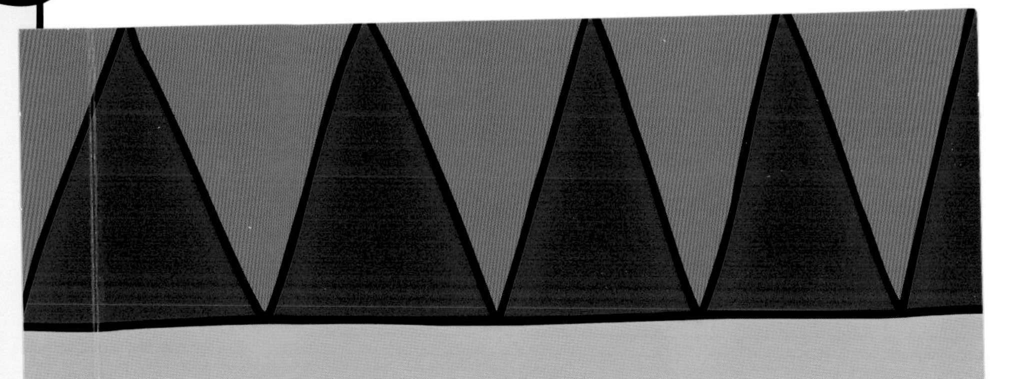

Write the missing letter to finish the words.

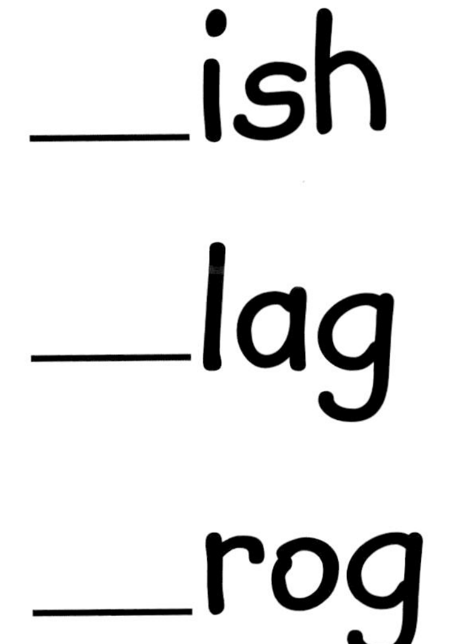

g
Girl starts with g and house starts with h. Help the little girl find her way home. She can only go through things beginning with g or h.
h

i
Write the missing letter to finish the words.
_ nk
_ ce-cream
_ gloo
jam
jumper
jar
jelly
j

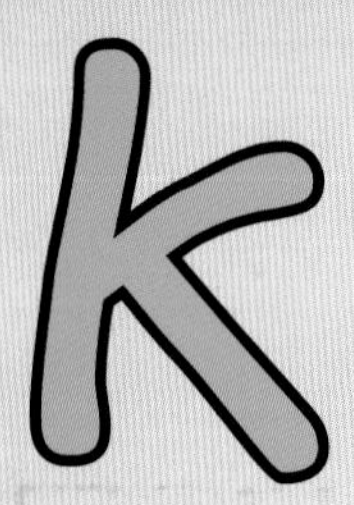

Look at the pictures and read the words.
Draw a circle around the odd one out in each line.

kite

king

kitten

leaf

lion

leg

l

m

Lift the flap to see who is hiding in the hole.
Which line leads to the cheese?

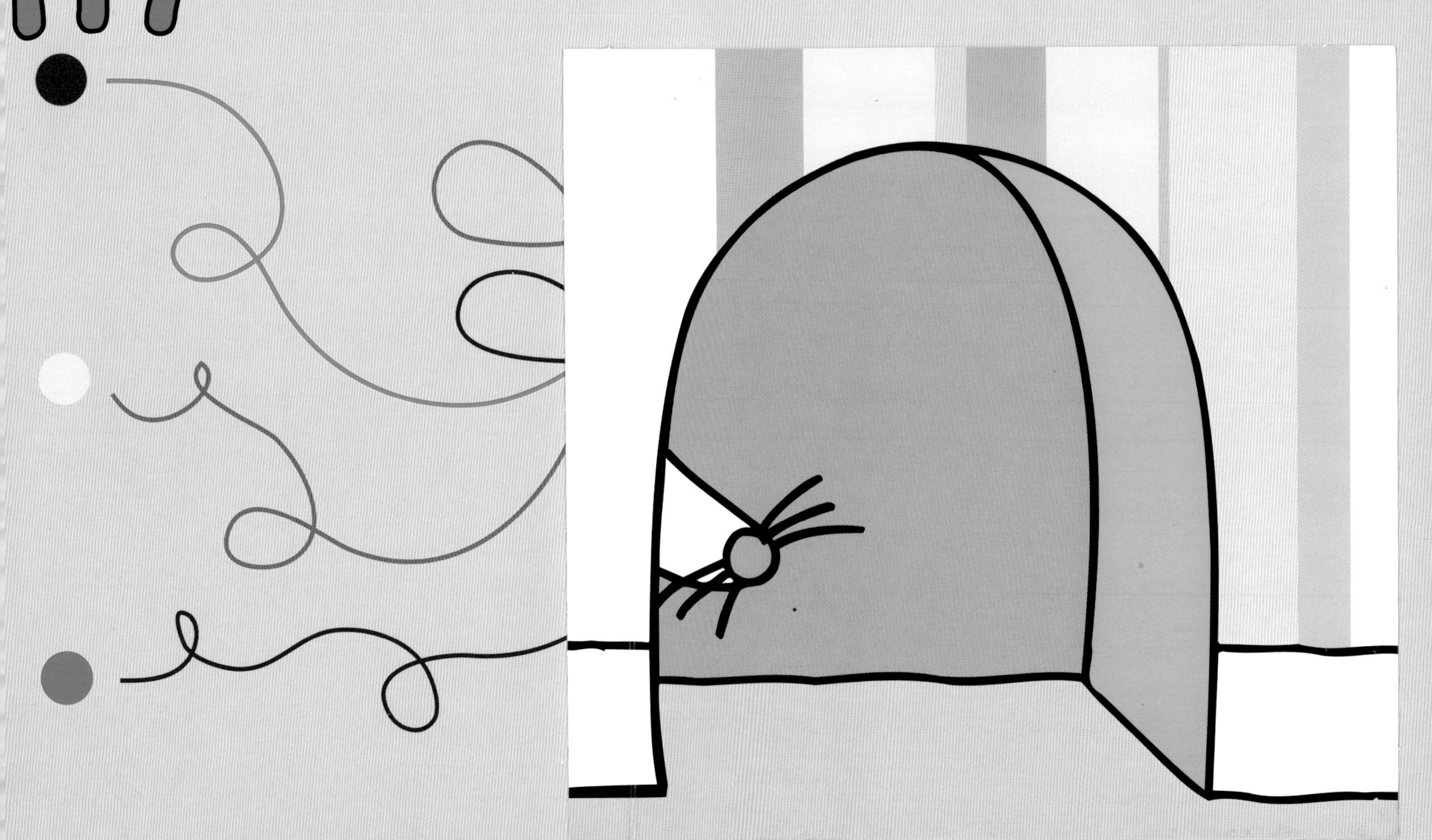

Which things begin with the letter m? Draw a circle around the things that begin with n. Colour in the picture.

Unscramble the letters to make a word beginning with the letter o. Look at the pictures to help you.

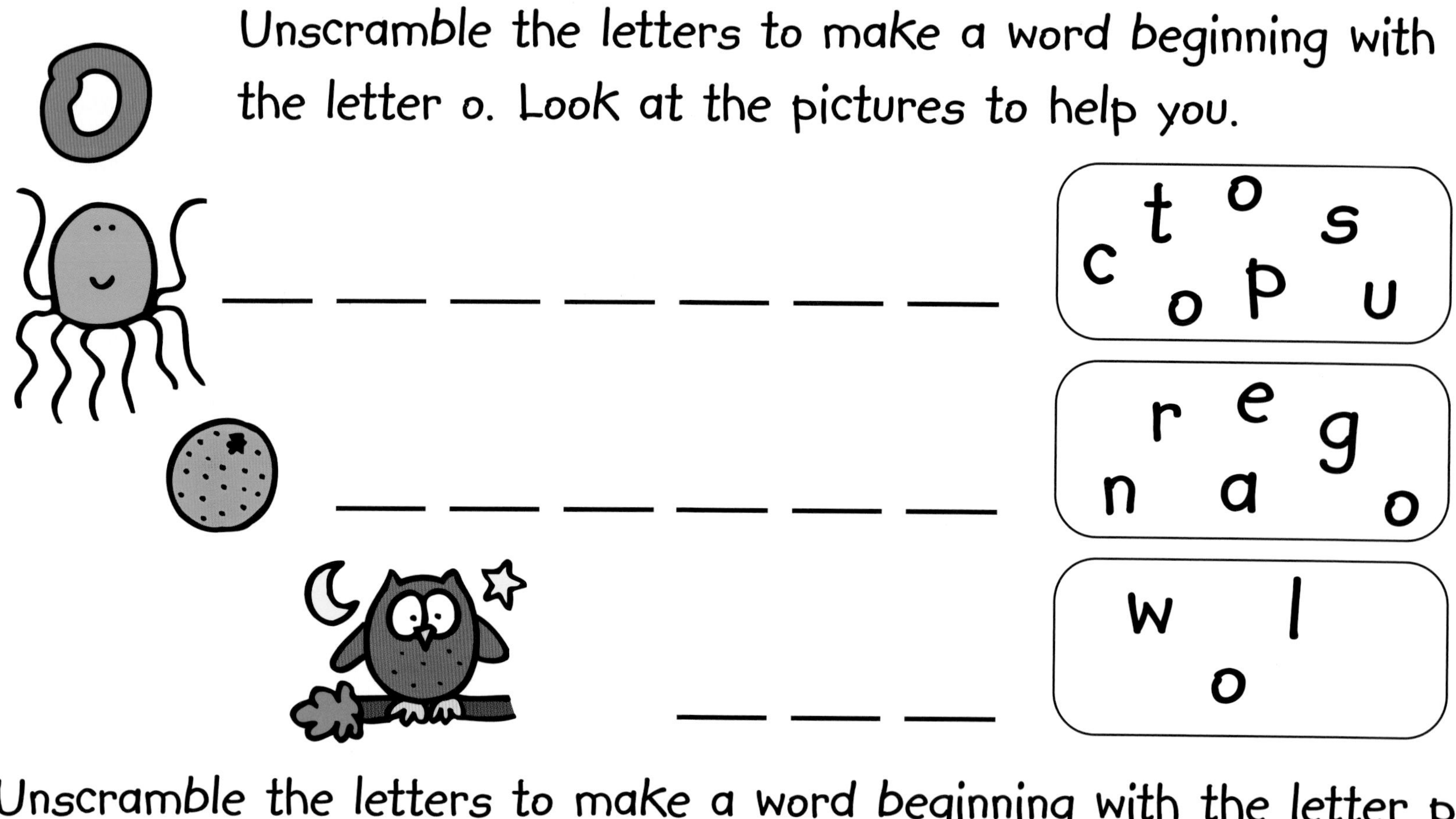

Unscramble the letters to make a word beginning with the letter p.

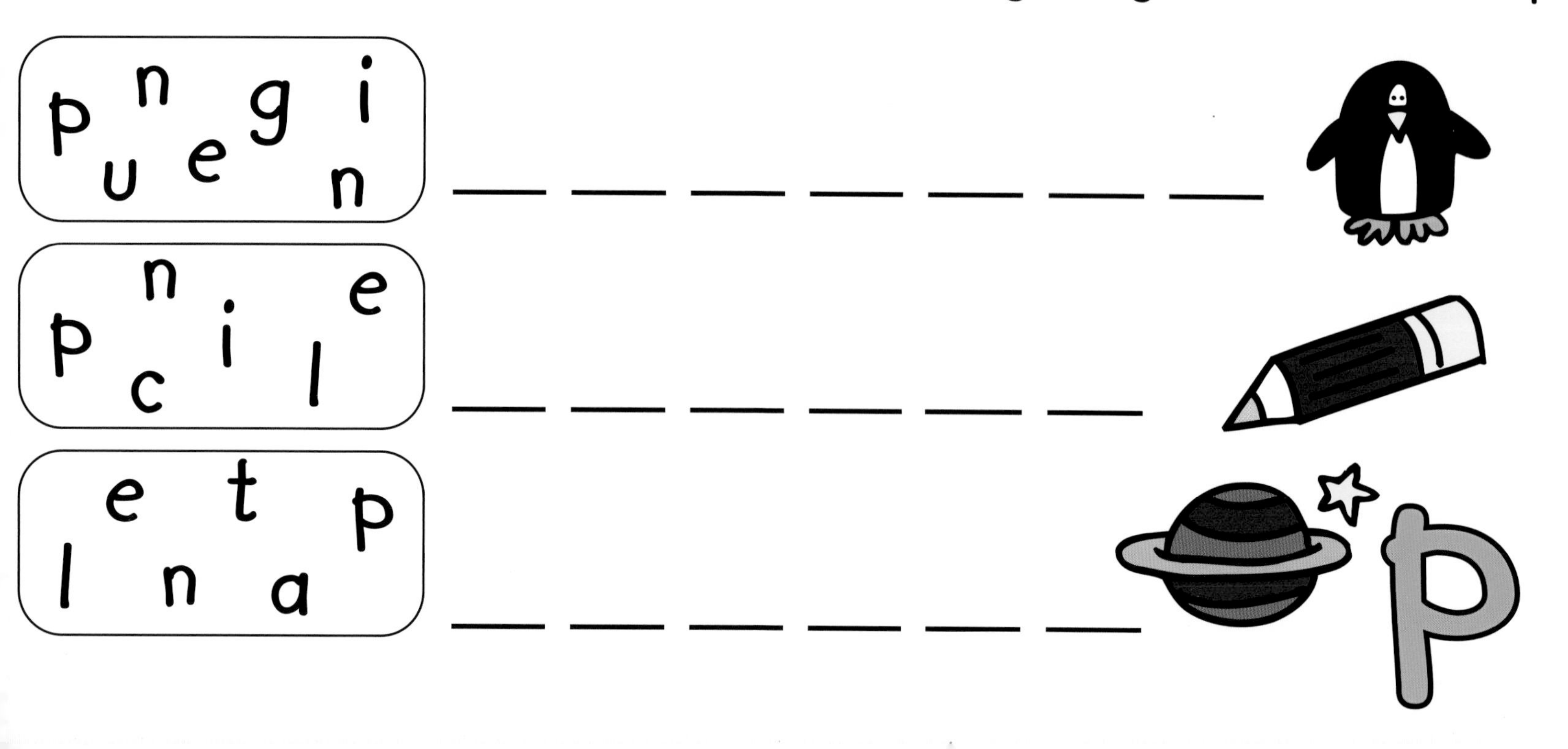

q

Queen, quilt, quiz, question and queue all start with q. Colour the people in the queue. What are they waiting for?

Which things begin with the letter r? Draw a circle around the odd one out. Colour in the picture.

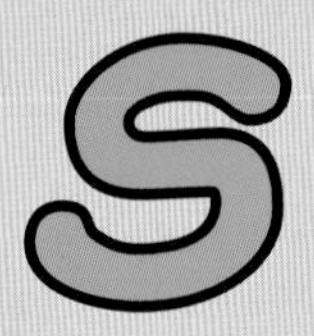

Sun, sock, snake, star and snail start with s.
Train, teddy, tree, tie and tiger start with t.

Draw lines to match each picture to its shadow. Circle the things that begin with t. Colour in the picture.

U

Umbrella starts with u. Draw some patterns on the umbrellas and colour them in.

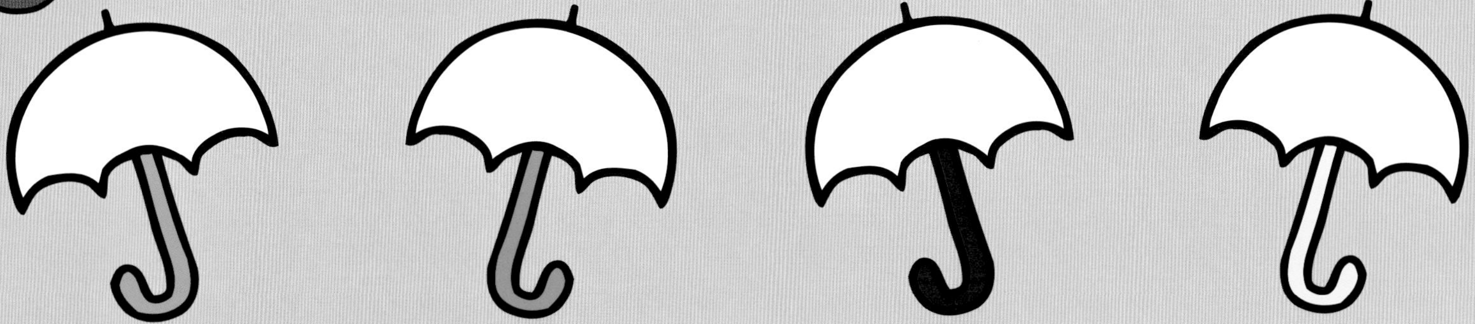

Write the letter to finish each word below.

v

___an ___et ___ase

W

How many things begin with the letter w? Colour them in.

Write the letter to finish the words.

fo ___

___-ray

bo___

X

y

Draw lines to match the yachts which are the same. Colour the one left over.

Zoo, zip, zero and zigzag start with z. Do you know an animal that begins with the letter z?

___ebra

z

Draw a line to match the pictures with the same beginning letter sound. Now colour them in.